# The Ballad of the Burglar of Babylon

# The Ballad of the

Woodcuts by Ann Grifalconi

# Elizabeth Bishop

# Burglar of Babylon

Farrar, Straus and Giroux    New York

*Text Copyright © 1964, 1968 by Elizabeth Bishop*
*Pictures Copyright © 1968 by Ann Grifalconi*
*Library of Congress catalog card number: 68-13681*
*All rights reserved*

FIRST PRINTING, *1968*

*Published simultaneously in Canada by*
*Ambassador Books, Ltd., Rexdale, Ontario*
*Printed in the United States of America*
*Designed by Ann Grifalconi and Herb Johnson*

The story of Micuçú* is true. It happened in Rio de Janeiro a few years ago. I have changed only one or two minor details, and, of course, translated the names of the slums. I think that actually the hill of Kerosene had been torn down shortly before Micuçú's death, but I liked the word, so put it in.

I was one of those who watched the pursuit through binoculars, although really we could see very little of it: just a few of the soldiers silhouetted against the skyline of the hill of Babylon. The rest of the story is taken, often word for word, from the daily papers, filled out by what I know of the place and the people.

At the time, people said that the name Micuçú was short for *Mico Sujo,* or *Dirty Marmoset,* but finally it was decided that this was wrong and that it is the colloquial name for a deadly snake, in the north of Brazil. A young man trying to be a real gangster, like in the films, would certainly prefer to be called by the name of a deadly snake. Also, the poor people who live in the slums of Rio have usually come from the north or northeast of Brazil and their nicknames are apt to be Indian words, or the common names (frequently derived from the Indian) used for things or creatures in those far-off regions.

E.B.

* Pronounced *mē-coo-soo.*

# The Ballad of the Burglar of Babylon

On the fair green hills of Rio
    There grows a fearful stain:
The poor who come to Rio
    And can't go home again.

On the hills a million people,
    A million sparrows, nest,
Like a confused migration
    That's had to light and rest,

Building its nests, or houses,
   Out of nothing at all, or air.
You'd think a breath would end them,
   They perch so lightly there.

But they cling and spread like lichen,
    And the people come and come.
There's one hill called the Chicken,
    And one called Catacomb;

There's the hill of Kerosene,
    And the hill of the Skeleton,
The hill of Astonishment,
    And the hill of Babylon.

Micuçú was a burglar and killer,
　　An enemy of society.
He had escaped three times
　　From the worst penitentiary.

They don't know how many he murdered
　　(Though they say he never raped),
And he wounded two policemen
　　This last time he escaped.

They said, "He'll go to his auntie,
　　Who raised him like a son.
She has a little drink shop
　　On the hill of Babylon."

He did go straight to his auntie,
And he drank a final beer.
He told her, "The soldiers are coming,
And I've got to disappear.

"Ninety years they gave me.
Who wants to live that long?
I'll settle for ninety hours,
On the hill of Babylon.

"Don't tell anyone you saw me.
I'll run as long as I can.
You were good to me, and I love you,
But I'm a doomed man."

Going out, he met a *mulata*
   Carrying water on her head.
"If you say you saw me, daughter,
   You're just as good as dead."

There are caves up there, and hideouts,
    And an old fort, falling down.
They used to watch for Frenchmen
    From the hill of Babylon.

Below him was the ocean.
    It reached far up the sky,
Flat as a wall, and on it
    Were freighters passing by,

Or climbing the wall, and climbing
Till each looked like a fly,
And then fell over and vanished;
And he knew he was going to die.

He could hear the goats *baa-baa*-ing,
   He could hear the babies cry;
Fluttering kites strained upward;
   And he knew he was going to die.

A buzzard flapped so near him
   He could see its naked neck.
He waved his arms and shouted,
   "Not yet, my son, not yet!"

An Army helicopter
Came nosing around and in.
He could see two men inside it,
But they never spotted him.

The soldiers were all over,
  On all sides of the hill,
And right against the skyline
  A row of them, small and still.

Children peeked out of windows,
  And men in the drink shop swore,
And spat a little *cachaça*
  At the light cracks in the floor.

But the soldiers were nervous, even
    With tommy guns in hand,
And one of them, in a panic,
    Shot the officer in command.

He hit him in three places;
    The other shots went wild.
The soldier had hysterics
    And sobbed like a little child.

The dying man said, "Finish
    The job we came here for."
He committed his soul to God
    And his sons to the Governor.

They ran and got a priest,
    And he died in hope of Heaven
—A man from Pernambuco,
    The youngest of eleven.

They wanted to stop the search,
But the Army said, "No, go on,"
So the soldiers swarmed again
Up the hill of Babylon.

Rich people in apartments
  Watched through binoculars
As long as the daylight lasted.
  And all night, under the stars,

Micuçú hid in the grasses
  Or sat in a little tree,
Listening for sounds, and staring
  At the lighthouse out at sea.

And the lighthouse stared back at him,
   Till finally it was dawn.
He was soaked with dew, and hungry,
   On the hill of Babylon.

The yellow sun was ugly,
   Like a raw egg on a plate—
Slick from the sea. He cursed it,
   For he knew it sealed his fate.

He saw the long white beaches
  And people going to swim,
With towels and beach umbrellas,
  But the soldiers were after him.

Far, far below, the people
  Were little colored spots,
And the heads of those in swimming
  Were floating coconuts.

He heard the peanut vender
Go *peep-peep* on his whistle,
And the man that sells umbrellas
Swinging his watchman's rattle.

Women with market baskets
   Stood on the corners and talked,
Then went on their way to market,
   Gazing up as they walked.

The rich with their binoculars
   Were back again, and many
Were standing on the rooftops,
   Among TV antennae.

It was early, eight or eight-thirty.
  He saw a soldier climb,
Looking right at him. He fired
  And missed for the last time.

He could hear the soldier panting,
  Though he never got very near.
Micuçú dashed for shelter.
  But he got it, behind the ear.

He heard the babies crying
Far, far away in his head,
And the mongrels barking and barking.
Then Micuçú was dead.

He had a Taurus revolver,
  And just the clothes he had on,
With two contos in the pockets,
  On the hill of Babylon.

The police and the populace
   Heaved a sigh of relief,
But behind the counter his auntie
   Wiped her eyes in grief.

"We have always been respected.
   My shop is honest and clean.
I loved him, but from a baby
   Micuçú was always mean.

"We have always been respected.
   His sister has a job.
Both of us gave him money.
   Why did he have to rob?

"I raised him to be honest,
   Even here, in Babylon slum."
The customers had another,
   Looking serious and glum.

But one of them said to another,
  When he got outside the door,
"He wasn't much of a burglar,
  He got caught six times—or more."

This morning the little soldiers
　　Are on Babylon hill again;
Their gun barrels and helmets
　　Shine in a gentle rain.

Micuçú is buried already.
　　They're after another two,
But they say they aren't as dangerous
　　As the poor Micuçú.

On the fair green hills of Rio
   There grows a fearful stain:
The poor who come to Rio
   And can't go home again.

There's the hill of Kerosene,
   And the hill of the Skeleton,
The hill of Astonishment,
   And the hill of Babylon.